JOHN THOMPSON'S
EASIEST PIANO COUR

FIRST JAZZ SONGS

This collection of jazz songs is intended as supplementary material for those working through **John Thompson's Easiest Piano Course** Parts 2–4. The pieces may also be used for sight reading practice by more advanced students.

Dynamics and phrasing have been deliberately omitted from the earlier pieces, since they are not introduced until Part 3 of the Easiest Piano Course, and initially the student's attention should be focused on playing notes and rhythms accurately. Outline fingering has been included, and in general the hand is assumed to remain in a five-finger position until a new fingering indicates a position shift. The fingering should suit most hands, although logical alternatives are always possible.

Is You Is Or Is You Ain't My Baby?

Words & Music by Billy Austin & Louis Jordan

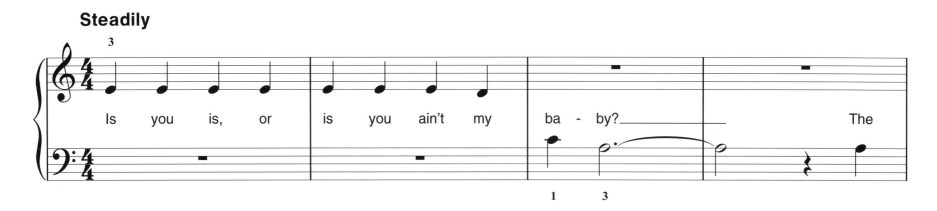

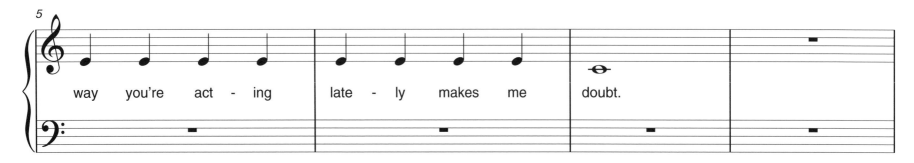

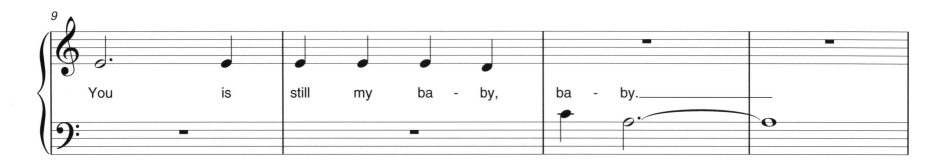

© Copyright 1943 Universal On Backstreet Music Inc.
Universal/MCA Music Limited.
All Rights Reserved. International Copyright Secured.

The Way You Look Tonight

Words by Dorothy Fields
Music by Jerome Kern

Gracefully

Some - day, when I'm aw - f'ly low, when the world is

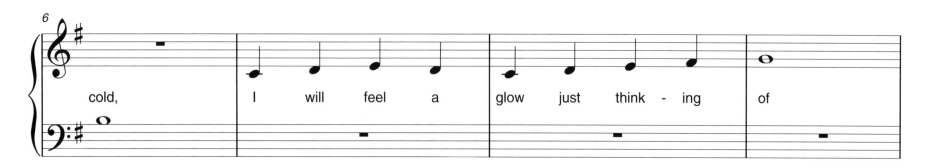

cold, I will feel a glow just think - ing of

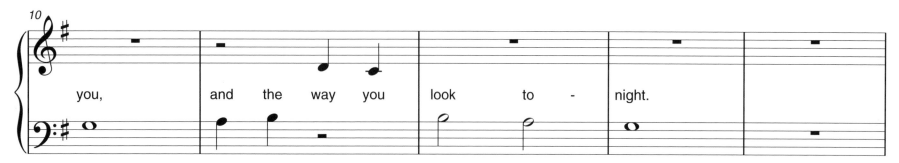

you, and the way you look to - night.

© Copyright 1936 Aldi Music Co., USA.
Shapiro Bernstein & Company Incorporated.
All Rights Reserved. International Copyright Secured.

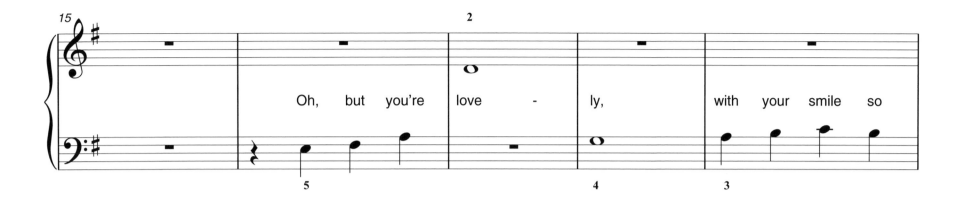

Oh, but you're love - ly, with your smile so

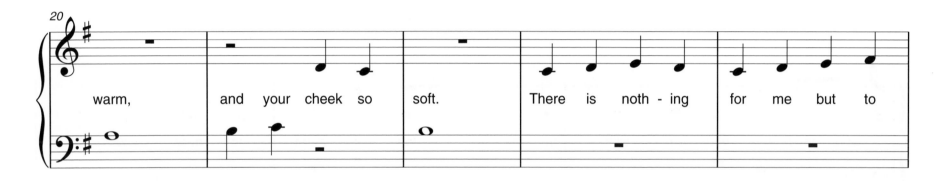

warm, and your cheek so soft. There is noth - ing for me but to

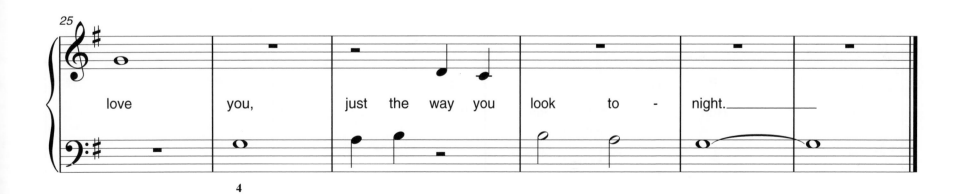

love you, just the way you look to - night.

Honeysuckle Rose

Words by Andy Razaf
Music by Thomas 'Fats' Waller

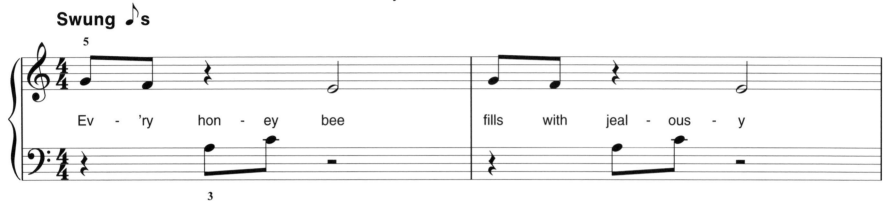

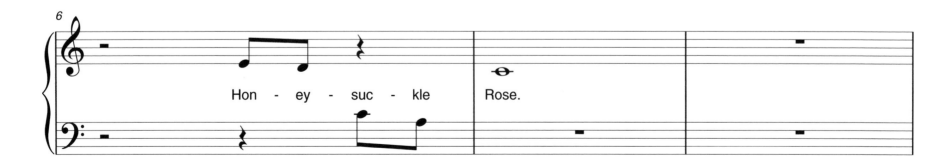

© Copyright 1929 Razaf Music.
Redwood Music Limited/BMG Rights Management (US) LLC.
All Rights Reserved. International Copyright Secured.

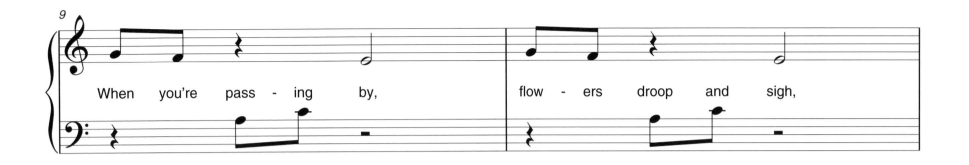

When you're pass - ing by, flow - ers droop and sigh,

and I know the rea - son why: you're much sweet - er, good - ness knows,

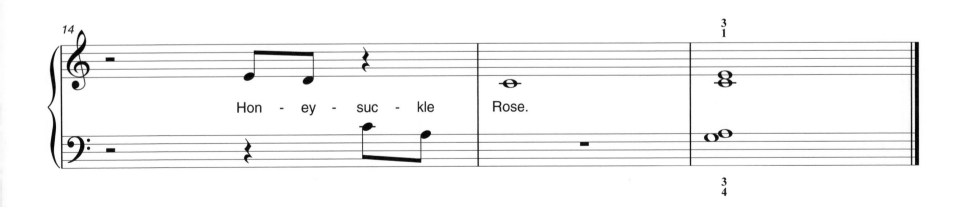

Hon - ey - suc - kle Rose.

Fly Me To The Moon (In Other Words)

Words & Music by Bart Howard

Cheerfully

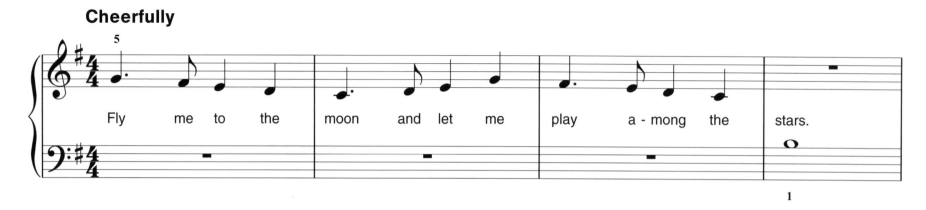

Fly me to the moon and let me play a - mong the stars.

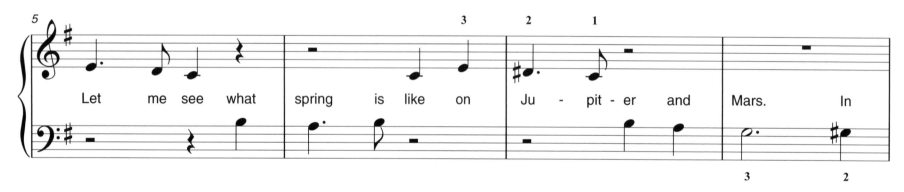

Let me see what spring is like on Ju - pit - er and Mars. In

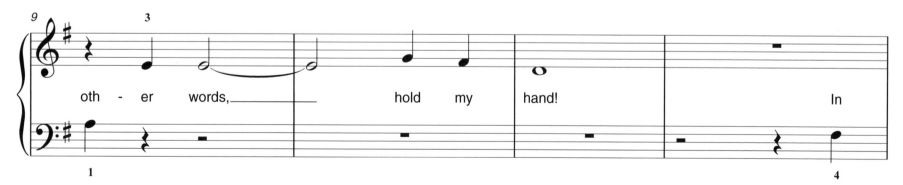

oth - er words, hold my hand! In

© Copyright 1954 Hampshire House Publishing Corporation.
TRO Essex Music Limited.
All Rights Reserved. International Copyright Secured.

As Time Goes By

Words & Music by Herman Hupfeld

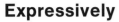

You must re-mem-ber this, a kiss is still a kiss, a sigh is just a sigh;_____ the

fun-da-men-tal things ap - ply as time goes by. And when two lov-ers woo, they

still say "I love you", on that you can re - ly,_____ no mat-ter what the fu - ture

© Copyright 1931 Redwood Music Limited.
All Rights Reserved. International Copyright Secured.

Ain't Misbehavin'

Words by Andy Razaf
Music by Thomas 'Fats' Waller & Harry Brooks

Slowly, swung ♪s

No one to talk with,_____ all by my - self;

no one to walk with, but I'm hap - py on the shelf.

Ain't mis - be - ha - vin',_____ I'm sa - vin' my love for you.

© Copyright 1929 Razaf Music.
Redwood Music Limited/BMG Rights Management (UK) Limited (Primary Wave).
All Rights Reserved. International Copyright Secured.

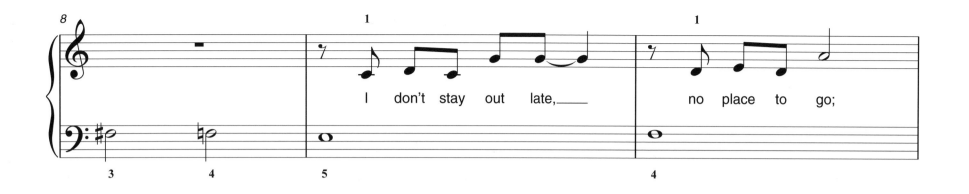

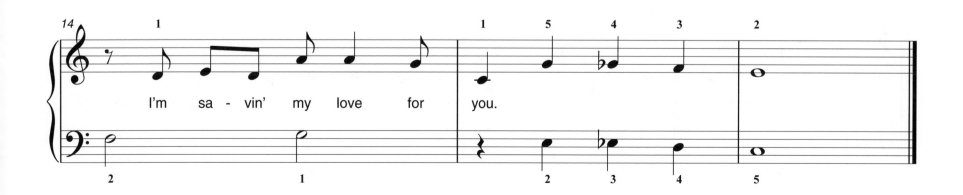

Hit The Road Jack

Words & Music by Percy Mayfield

© Copyright 1961 Tangerine Music Corporation, USA.
Kassner Associated Publishers Limited.
All Rights Reserved. International Copyright Secured.

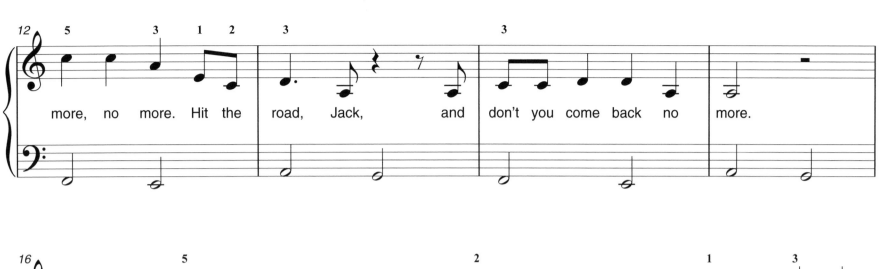

more, no more. Hit the road, Jack, and don't you come back no more.

Hit the road, Jack, and don't you come back no more, no more, no

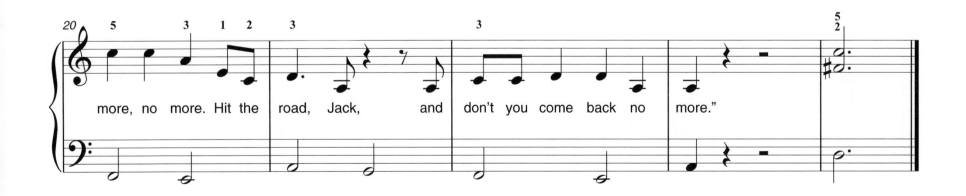

more, no more. Hit the road, Jack, and don't you come back no more."

The Girl From Ipanema

Words by Norman Gimbel & Vinicius De Moraes
Music by Antonio Carlos Jobim

© Copyright 1963 Universal Music Publishing Limited/Hal Leonard LLC.
All Rights Reserved. International Copyright Secured.

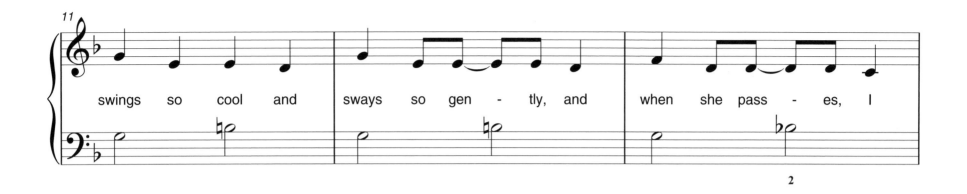

swings so cool and sways so gen - tly, and when she pass - es, I

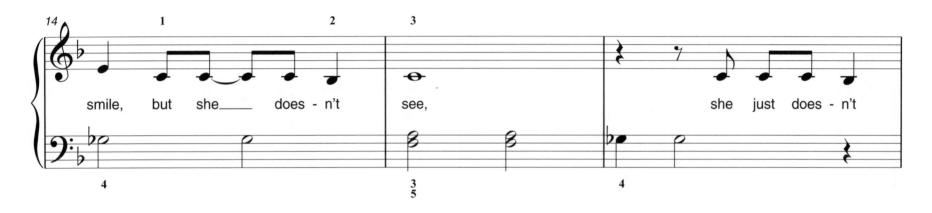

smile, but she___ does - n't see, she just does - n't

see, no, she does - n't see.

Taking A Chance On Love

Words by John La Touche & Ted Fetter
Music by Vernon Duke

© Copyright 1940 EMI Miller Catalog Incorporated.
EMI United Partnership Limited.
All Rights Reserved. International Copyright Secured.

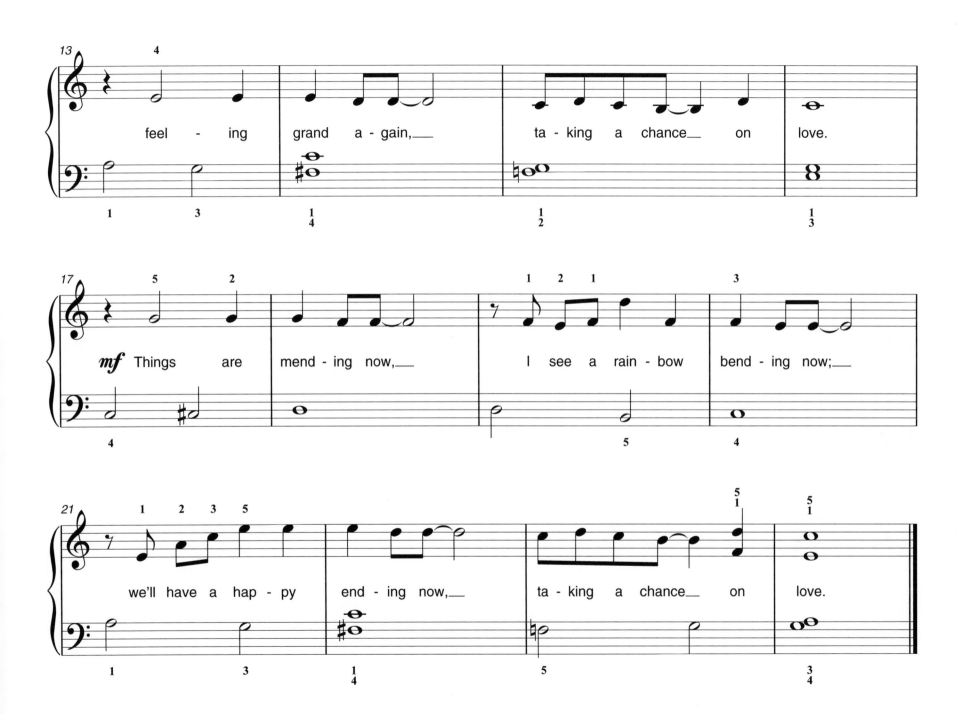

feel - ing grand a - gain,___ ta - king a chance___ on love.

mf Things are mend - ing now,___ I see a rain - bow bend - ing now;___

we'll have a hap - py end - ing now,___ ta - king a chance___ on love.

I'm Beginning To See The Light

Words & Music by Duke Ellington, Harry James, Johnny Hodges & Don George

© Copyright 1944 Grand Music Corporation, USA/Alamo Music Incorporated.
Chester Music Limited trading as Campbell Connelly & Co. for British Commonwealth (excluding Australia/Canada/New Zealand) and Europe/Redwood Music Limited for British Commonwealth, Ireland and Spain.
All Rights Reserved. International Copyright Secured.

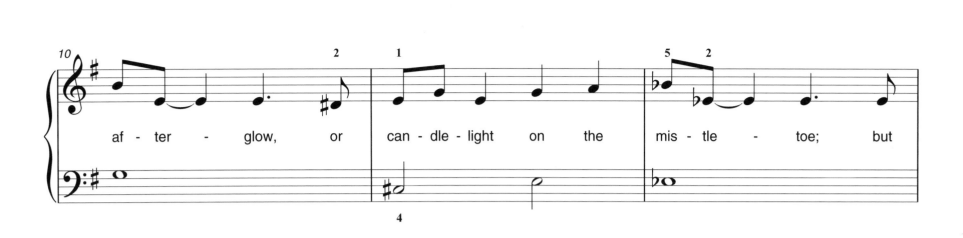

af - ter - glow, or can - dle - light on the mis - tle - toe; but

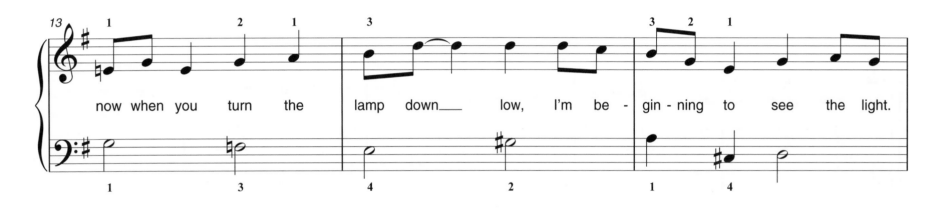

now when you turn the lamp down____ low, I'm be - gin - ning to see the light.

f I'm be - gin - ning to see the light.

Corcovado (Quiet Nights Of Quiet Stars)

Words & Music by Antonio Carlos Jobim

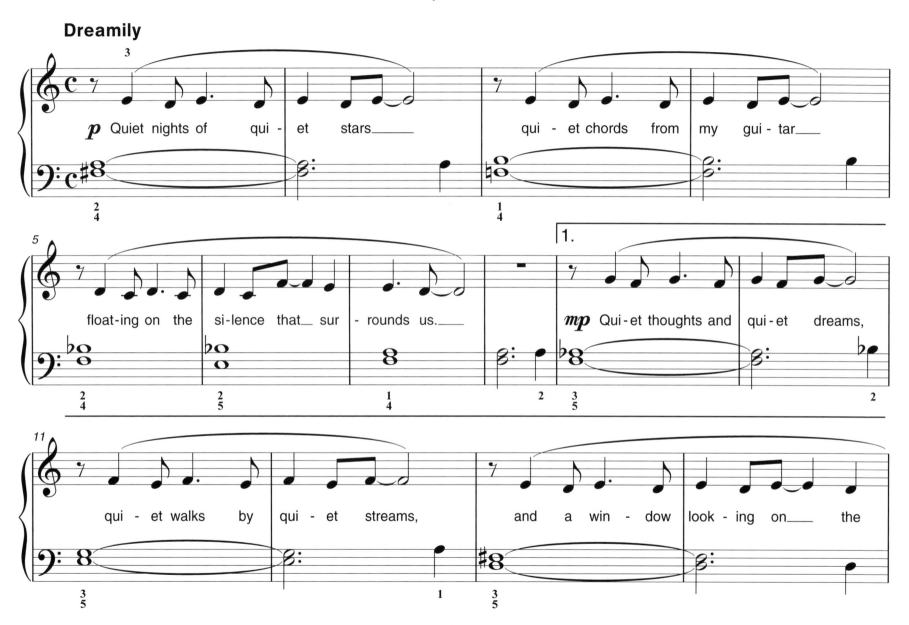

© Copyright 1962 Songs Of Universal Incorporated.
Universal/MCA Music Limited.
All Rights Reserved. International Copyright Secured.

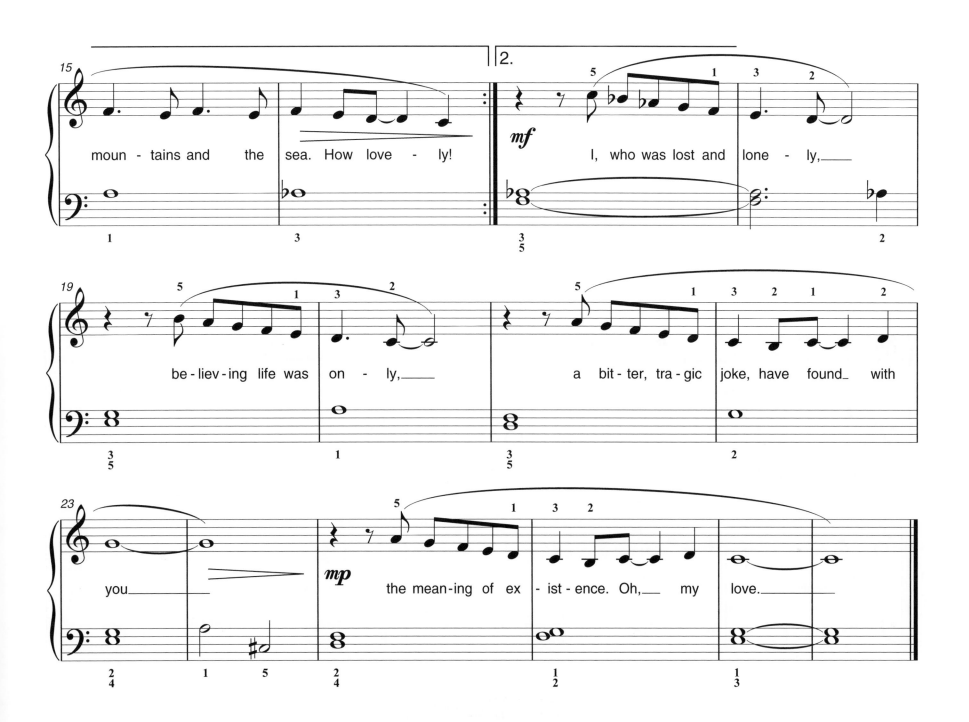

23

Georgia On My Mind

Words by Stuart Gorrell
Music by Hoagy Carmichael

© Copyright 1930, Renewed 1957 Southern Music Publishing Company Incorporated.
Administered by Chester Music Limited trading as Campbell Connelly & Co. for UK, Eire, Belgium, France, Holland, Switzerland, Fiji, Gibraltar, Hong Kong, Malaysia, Saint Helena, Sierra Leone, Singapore and Sri Lanka.
All Rights Reserved. International Copyright Secured.

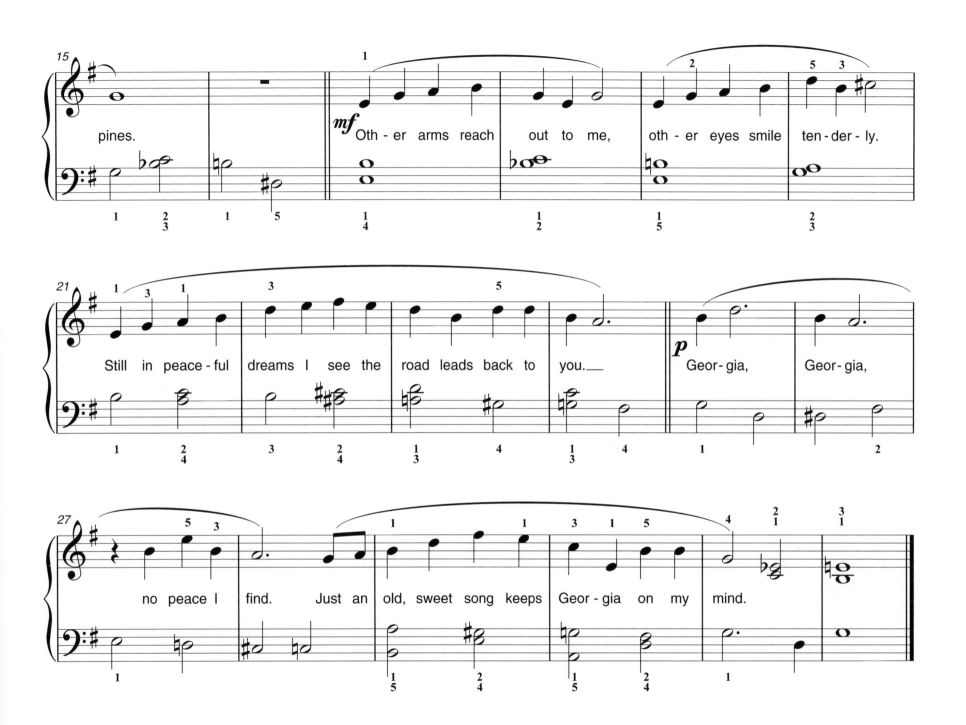

St Louis Blues

Words & Music by William C. Handy

© Copyright 1914 Francis Day & Hunter Limited.
All Rights Reserved. International Copyright Secured.

St. Lou - is blues, just as blue as___ I___ can be.___   That___

man got a heart like a rock cast___ in___ the sea.___   Or___

else he___ would - n't have gone so___ far from___ me.___   *mp*

27

I Can't Get Started

Words by Ira Gershwin
Music by Vernon Duke

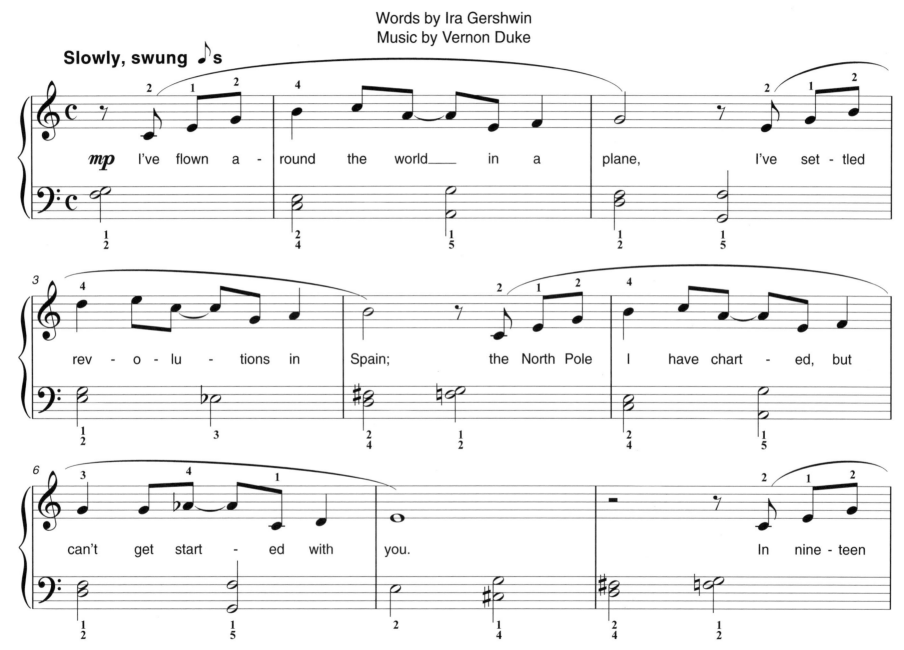

© Copyright 1935 Kay Duke Music/Ira Gershwin Music.
Universal/MCA Music Limited/Warner/Chappell North America Limited.
All Rights Reserved. International Copyright Secured.

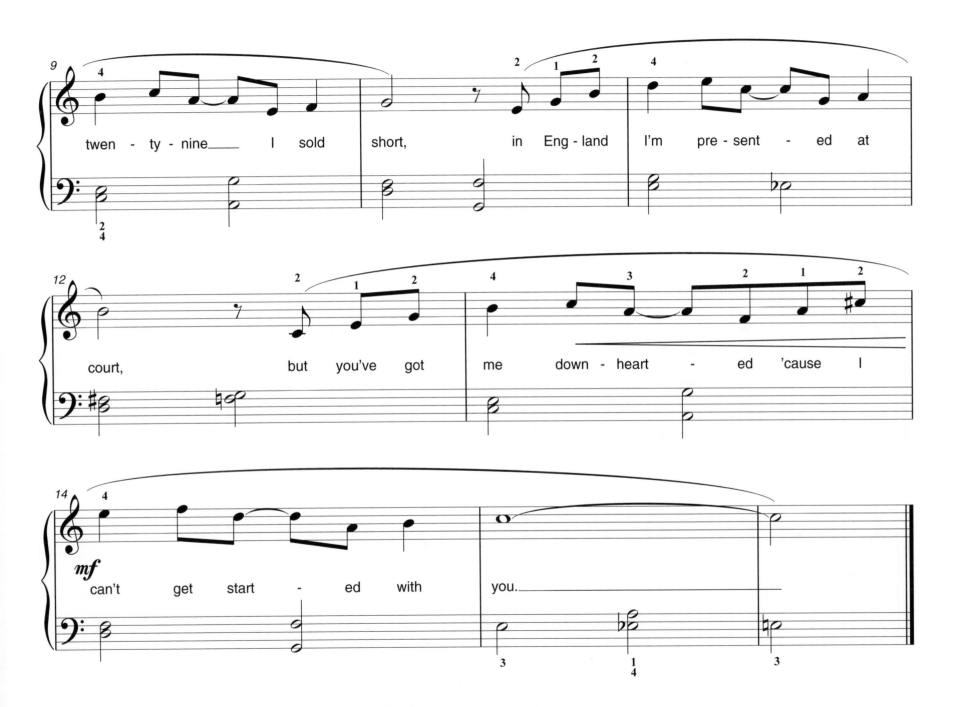

St Thomas

Music by Sonny Rollins

Crisply and rhythmically

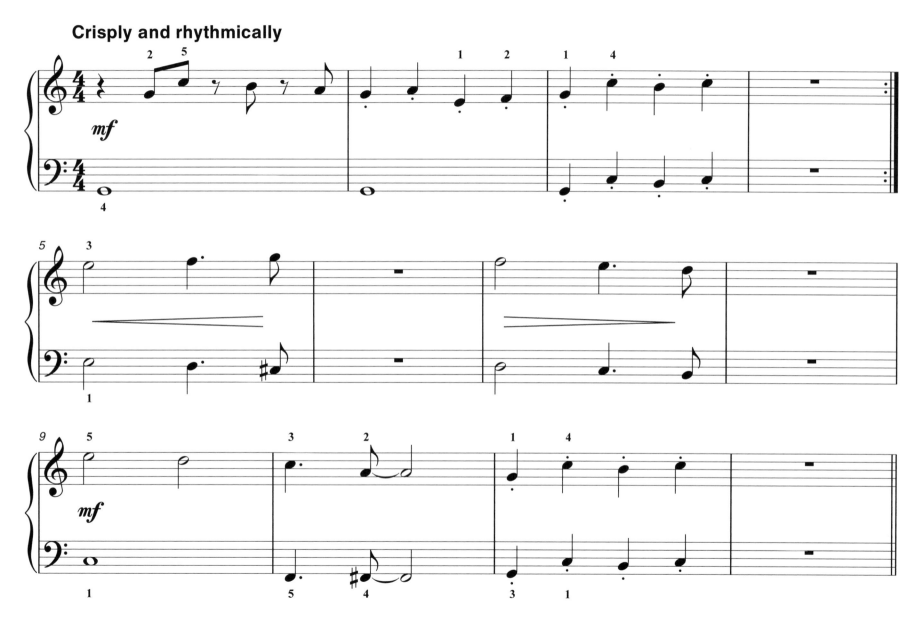

© Copyright 1963 Prestige Music Company Incorporated, USA.
Prestige Music Limited.
All Rights Reserved. International Copyright Secured.

123456789

31

© Copyright 2017 The Willis Music Company
Florence, Kentucky, USA. All Rights Reserved.

Exclusive Distributors:
Music Sales Limited
Newmarket Road, Bury St Edmunds, Suffolk IP33 3YB, UK.

Order No. WMR101838
ISBN: 978-1-78558-530-2

Unauthorised reproduction of any part of this publication by any means
including photocopying is an infringement of copyright.

Arranged by Christopher Hussey.
Arrangements and engravings supplied by Camden Music Services.
Cover illustration by Sergio Sandoval.

Printed in the EU.